The Joy of Organ Music

The Joy Of Organ Music embodies a colorful well-balanced

repertoire of easy to play melodies. Of particular interest

are the familiar themes by the masters, folk tunes,

favorite standard songs and popular melodies of today.

The skilful, full-sounding arrangements by Nelson Varon

are intended for the beginning or early-intermediate

grade player; they are most appealing in their simplicity

and interesting enough to prepare and inspire the player

for more advanced study.

Suggested registrations are found at the beginning of each

piece with additional general instructions on Page 3.

Distributed throughout the world by
Music Sales, 257 Park Avenue South, New York, N.Y. 10010, U.S.A.
Music Sales, 8/9 Frith Street, London W1V 5TZ, England.
Music Sales, 120 Rothschild Street, Rosebery, NSW 2018, Australia.

Printed in Great Britain by J.B. Offset Ltd.

Contents

INSTRUCTIONS FOR USING
ALL ORGAN REGISTRATIONS

I. Electronic Organs:

When registration calls for a stop which is not on your particular electronic organ use a similar sounding stop in the *same footage*. For example, if the registration calls for an 8′ String and your organ does not have a stop called String—use a Violin 8′, or Viola 8′, or Salicional 8′ etc.

II. Hammond Pre-Set Console Models:
Permanently set as follows:

UPPER Ⓑ and LOWER A#

and use Drawbar registrations as indicated

III. M-100 and L-100 Hammond Spinet Models:
Set the tablets permanently as follows:

M-100 SERIES

PEDAL   PERCUSSION   VIBRATO   LOWER MANUAL   UPPER MANUAL   REV.   VOL.

L-100 SERIES

LOWER   UPPER   PERCUSSION   VIBRATO   REV.   VOL.

and use Drawbar registrations for Upper and Lower manuals and for Pedal as indicated at each selection.

IV. On all Hammond Spinet Models:

Disregard parenthesized numerals when you do not have that drawbar on your model organ, but *use* the paranthesized numeral if your model spinet *does* have the additional Drawbar.

Fascination

ELECTRONIC ORGANS
Upper: String 8′
Lower: Melodia 8′
Pedal: 8′
Vibrato: On Full

DRAWBAR ORGANS
Upper: 00 8222-232
Lower: (00) 4302-000 (0)
Pedal: 3 (2)
Vibrato: On Full

Slow Waltz

Filippo D. Marchetti

© Copyright 1904 F. D. Marchetti
© Copyright 1936 J. Liber, London
© Copyright 1954 Liber–Southern Ltd,
8 Denmark Street, London WC2

Parade Of The Tin Soldiers

ELECTRONIC ORGANS
Upper: Trumpet 8′   Pedal: 8′
Lower: Diapason 8′   Vibrato: On Full

DRAWBAR ORGANS
Upper: 00-7677-540   Pedal: 4 (3)
Lower: (00)-5431-210 (0)   Vibrato: On Full

Leon Jessel

Lively walking tempo

PARADE OF THE TIN SOLDIERS - Jessel

Copyright 1912 by Hawkes & Son (London) Ltd. as sole agents for Heinrichshofen's Verlag for the British Commonwealth.
This edition authorised for sale in the United Kingdom and The Republic of Ireland by permission of Boosey & Hawkes Music Publishers Ltd.

Moscow Nights

ELECTRONIC ORGANS
Upper: Trumpet 8′ Pedal: 8′
Lower: Diapason 8′ Vibrato: On Full

DRAWBAR ORGANS
Upper: 00-7677-540 Pedal: 4 (3)
Lower: (00)-5431-210 (0) Vibrato: On Full

V. Soloviev - Sedoy

The Whistler And His Dog

ELECTRONIC ORGANS
Upper: Flute 8′
Lower: Melodia 8′
Pedal: 8′
Vibrato: On Full

DRAWBAR ORGANS
Upper: 008200-000
Lower: (00) 4302-000 (0)
Pedal: 3 (2)
Vibrato: On Full

Arthur Pryor

Estrellita

ELECTRONIC ORGANS
Upper: String 8′ Pedal: 8′
Lower: Melodia 8′ Vibrato: On Full

DRAWBAR ORGANS
Upper: 00 8222-232 Pedal: 3 (2)
Lower: (00) 4302-000 (0) Vibrato: On Full

Manuel M. Ponce

Slowly, with feeling

ESTRELLITA - Ponce
Copyright 1914 by M. Ponce.
Copyright Owners for the British Commonwealth, the Republic of Ireland
and the Republic of South Africa Hawkes & Son (London) Ltd. by arrangement
with W. Bessel & Cie, Paris.
This edition authorised for sale in the United Kingdom and The Republic of
Ireland by permission of Boosey & Hawkes Music Publishers Ltd.

Clarinet Polka

ELECTRONIC ORGANS
Upper: Clarinet 8′   Pedal: 8′
Lower: Melodia 8′   Vibrato: On Full

DRAWBAR ORGANS
Upper: 00-8040-400   Pedal 3 (2)
Lower: (00) 43-03-000 (0)   Vibrato: On Full

Traditional

Elegie

ELECTRONIC ORGANS
Upper: Clarinet 8′   Pedal: 8′
Lower: Melodia 8′   Vibrato: On Full

DRAWBAR ORGANS
Upper: 00-8040-400   Pedal 3 (2)
Lower: (00) 43-03-000 (0)   Vibrato: On Full

Jules Massenet

Slowly

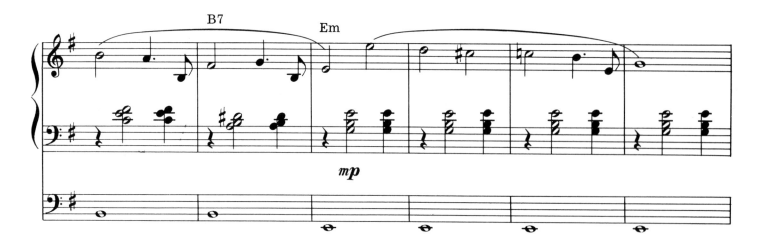

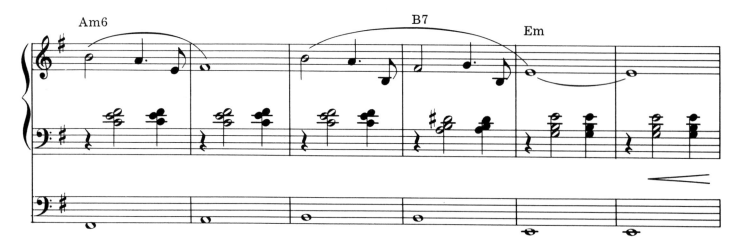

Adios Muchachos

ELECTRONIC ORGANS
Upper: Flutes 16', 8' 4'
      Strings 8'
      Reed 8'
Lower: Melodia 8'
      Diapason 8'

Pedal: 16', 8'
Vibrato: On Full

DRAWBAR ORGANS
Upper: 60-8856-364
Lower: (00) 6523-454 (0)

Pedal: 6 (4)
Vibrato: On Full

Julio Sanders

Moderate Tango

Arkansas Traveler

ELECTRONIC ORGANS
Upper: String 8′   Pedal: 8′
Lower: Melodia 8′   Vibrato: On Full

DRAWBAR ORGANS
Upper: 00 8222-232   Pedal: 3 (2)
Lower: (00) 4302-000 (0) Vibrato: On Full

Traditional

A Touch Of Blues

ELECTRONIC ORGANS
Upper: String 8′   Pedal: 8′
Lower: Melodia 8′   Vibrato: On Full

DRAWBAR ORGANS
Upper: 00 8222-232   Pedal: 3 (2)
Lower: (00) 4302-000 (0)   Vibrato: On Full

Gerald Martin

Slow, lazy beat

Boogie Woogie Martian Star

ELECTRONIC ORGANS
Upper: Flutes 16′, 8′ 4′   Pedal: 16′, 8′
        Strings 8′   Vibrato: On Full
        Reed 8′
Lower: Melodia 8′
        Diapason 8′

DRAWBAR ORGANS
Upper: 60-8856-364   Pedal: 6 (4)
Lower: (00) 6523-454 (0)   Vibrato: On Full

Moderately, with a strong beat

Nelson Varon

Chicken Reel

ELECTRONIC ORGANS
Upper: String 8′   Pedal: 8′
Lower: Melodia 8′   Vibrato: On Full

DRAWBAR ORGANS
Upper: 00 8222-232   Pedal: 3 (2)
Lower: (00) 4302-000 (0)   Vibrato: On Full

Lively   Traditional

The Cowboy's Lament

(The Streets of Laredo)

ELECTRONIC ORGANS
Upper: Trumpet 8′
Lower: Diapason 8′
Pedal: 8′
Vibrato: On Full

DRAWBAR ORGANS
Upper: 00-7677-540
Lower: (00)-5431-210 (0)
Pedal: 4 (3)
Vibrato: On Full

Folk Song

Londonderry Air

ELECTRONIC ORGANS
Upper: Flute 8′   Pedal: 8′
Lower: Melodia 8′   Vibrato: On Full

DRAWBAR ORGANS
Upper: 008200-000   Pedal: 3 (2)
Lower: (00) 4302-000 (0)   Vibrato: On Full

Irish Song.

Down In The Valley

ELECTRONIC ORGANS
Upper: Flute 8′
Lower: Melodia 8′
Pedal: 8′
Vibrato: On Full

DRAWBAR ORGANS
Upper: 008200-000
Lower: (00) 4302-000 (0)
Pedal: 3 (2)
Vibrato: On Full

Gently moving

Folk Song

Marian

ELECTRONIC ORGANS
Upper: Trumpet 8′   Pedal: 8′
Lower: Diapason 8′   Vibrato: On Full

DRAWBAR ORGANS
Upper: 00-7677-540   Pedal: 4 (3)
Lower: (00)-5431-210 (0)   Vibrato: On Full

Moderate

Calypso Song

Lyrics:

All day, all night, Ma-ri-an, Down by sea-side sift-ing sand.

Ev-'ry-one loves Ma-ri-an, Down by sea-side sift-ing sand. *Fine*

Why don't you come down to Tri-ni-dad; You'll have the best time you ev-er had.

'Cause ev-'ry-thing is so ver-y nice, Come on and see this is-land par-a-dise. *D.C. al Fine*

Greensleeves

ELECTRONIC ORGANS
Upper: String 8'   Pedal: 8'
Lower: Melodia 8'   Vibrato: On Full

DRAWBAR ORGANS
Upper: 00 8222-232   Pedal: 3 (2)
Lower: (00) 4302-000 (0) Vibrato: On Full

Moderately

English Folk Song

Careless Love

ELECTRONIC ORGANS
Upper: Clarinet 8′   Pedal: 8′
Lower: Melodia 8′   Vibrato: On Full

DRAWBAR ORGANS
Upper: 00-8040-400   Pedal 3 (2)
Lower: (00) 43-03-000 (0)   Vibrato: On Full

Moderately

Folk Song

Love, oh love, oh care-less love,

Love, oh love, oh care-less love,

Love, oh love, oh care-less love, Just

see what love has done to me.

Lullaby

ELECTRONIC ORGANS
Upper: Flute 8′   Pedal: 8′
Lower: Melodia 8′   Vibrato: On Full

DRAWBAR ORGANS
Upper: 008200-000   Pedal: 3 (2)
Lower: (00) 4302-000 (0)   Vibrato: On Full

Johannes Brahms

Hungarian Dance No. 4

ELECTRONIC ORGANS
Upper: String 8′   Pedal: 8′
Lower: Melodia 8′   Vibrato: On Full

DRAWBAR ORGANS
Upper: 00 8222-232   Pedal: 3 (2)
Lower: (00) 4302-000 (0)   Vibrato: On Full

Johannes Brahms

Träumerei

ELECTRONIC ORGANS
Upper: String 8′   Pedal: 8′
Lower: Melodia 8′   Vibrato: On Full

DRAWBAR ORGANS
Upper: 00 8222-232   Pedal: 3 (2)
Lower: (00) 4302-000 (0) Vibrato: On Full

Robert Schumann

Slowly, with feeling

Waltz

ELECTRONIC ORGANS
Upper: Clarinet 8' Pedal: 8'
Lower: Melodia 8' Vibrato: On Full

DRAWBAR ORGANS
Upper: 00-8040-400 Pedal 3 (2)
Lower: (00) 43-03-000 (0) Vibrato: On Full

Johannes Brahms

Slowly

D.C. al Fine

Pomp and Circumstance

ELECTRONIC ORGANS
Upper: Flutes 16′, 8′ 4′   Pedal: 16′, 8′
     Strings 8′   Vibrato: On Full
     Reed 8′
Lower: Melodia 8′
     Diapason 8′

DRAWBAR ORGANS
Upper: 60-8856-364   Pedal: 6 (4)
Lower: (00) 6523-454 (0)   Vibrato: On Full

Edward Elgar

Broadly

Sheep May Safely Graze

ELECTRONIC ORGANS
Upper: Trumpet 8'   Pedal: 8'
Lower: Diapason 8'   Vibrato: On Full

DRAWBAR ORGANS
Upper: 00-7677-540   Pedal: 4 (3)
Lower: (00)-5431-210 (0)   Vibrato: On Full

Gently moving

Johann Sebastian Bach

Arioso

ELECTRONIC ORGANS
Upper: String 8′ Pedal: 8′
Lower: Melodia 8′ Vibrato: On Full

DRAWBAR ORGANS
Upper: 00 8222-232 Pedal: 3 (2)
Lower: (00) 4302-000 (0) Vibrato: On Full

Johann Sebastian Bach

Slowly

Nocturne

ELECTRONIC ORGANS
Upper: String 8′ Pedal: 8′
Lower: Melodia 8′ Vibrato: On Full

DRAWBAR ORGANS
Upper: 00 8222-232 Pedal: 3 (2)
Lower: (00) 4302-000 (0) Vibrato: On Full

Slowly, with expression

Frederic Chopin

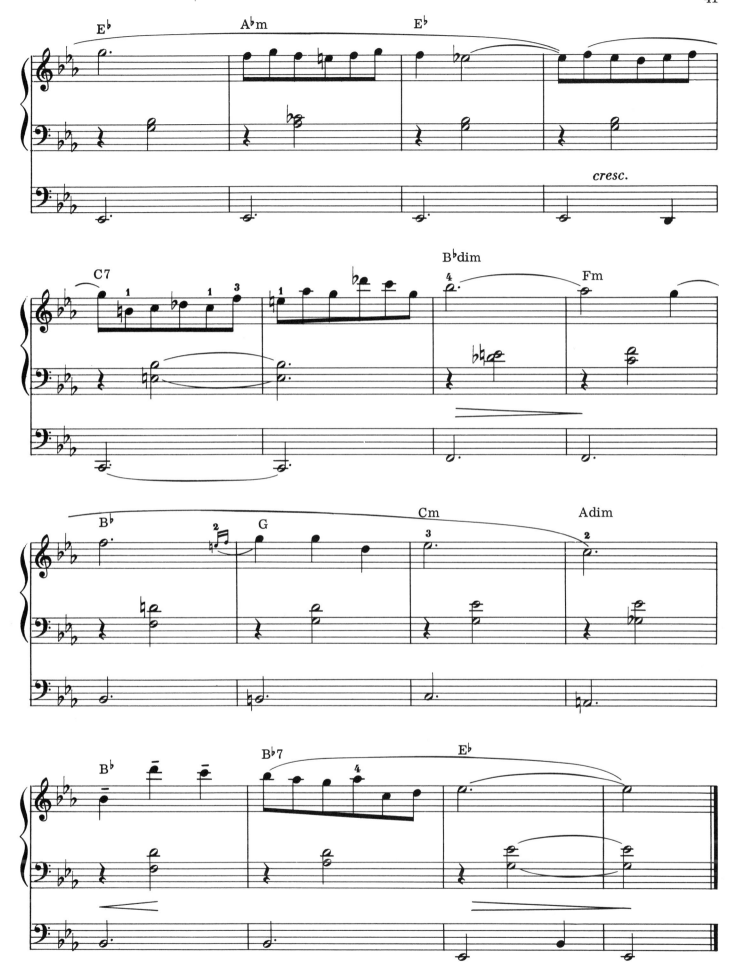

Clair De Lune

ELECTRONIC ORGANS
Upper: Flute 8′   Pedal: 8′
Lower: Melodia 8′   Vibrato: On Full

DRAWBAR ORGANS
Upper: 008200-000   Pedal: 3 (2)
Lower: (00) 4302-000 (0)   Vibrato: On Full

Slowly, with expression

Claude Debussy

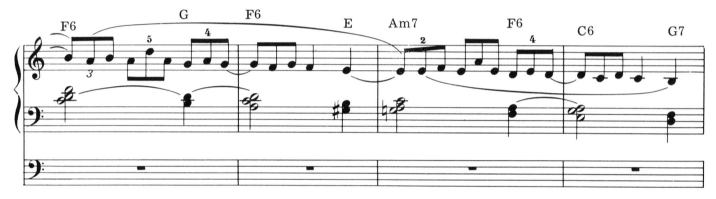

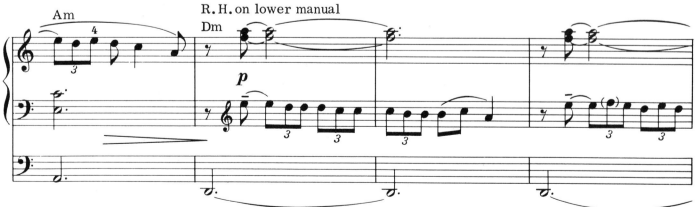

Theme from "Pathetique Symphony"

ELECTRONIC ORGANS
Upper: String 8' Pedal: 8'
Lower: Melodia 8' Vibrato: On Full

DRAWBAR ORGANS
Upper: 00 8222-232 Pedal: 3 (2)
Lower: (00) 4302-000 (0) Vibrato: On Full

Peter I. Tchaikovsky

I Love Thee

ELECTRONIC ORGANS
Upper: Clarinet 8′ Pedal: 8′
Lower: Melodia 8′ Vibrato: On Full

DRAWBAR ORGANS
Upper: 00-8040-400 Pedal 3 (2)
Lower: (00) 43-03-000 (0) Vibrato: On Full

Edvard Grieg

Slowly, with expression

Ave Maria

ELECTRONIC ORGANS
Upper: String 8′ Pedal: 8′
Lower: Melodia 8′ Vibrato: On Full

DRAWBAR ORGANS
Upper: 00 8222-232 Pedal: 3 (2)
Lower: (00) 4302-000 (0) Vibrato: On Full

Bach - Gounod

My Heart At Thy Sweet Voice

from "Samson and Delilah"

ELECTRONIC ORGANS
Upper: Flute 8′   Pedal: 8′
Lower: Melodia 8′   Vibrato: On Full

DRAWBAR ORGANS
Upper: 008200-000   Pedal: 3 (2)
Lower: (00) 4302-000 (0)   Vibrato: On Full

Camille Saint - Saens

To A Wild Rose

ELECTRONIC ORGANS
Upper: Flute 8′   Pedal: 8′
Lower: Melodia 8′   Vibrato: On Full

DRAWBAR ORGANS
Upper: 008200-000   Pedal: 3 (2)
Lower: (00) 4302-000 (0)   Vibrato: On Full

Edward MacDowell

With simple tenderness

Musetta's Waltz

from "La Boheme"

ELECTRONIC ORGANS
Upper: String 8'   Pedal: 8'
Lower: Melodia 8'   Vibrato: On Full

DRAWBAR ORGANS
Upper: 00 8222-232   Pedal: 3 (2)
Lower: (00) 4302-000 (0)   Vibrato: On Full

Giacomo Puccini

The Emperor Waltz

ELECTRONIC ORGANS
Upper: Flutes 16′, 8′ 4′
      Strings 8′
      Reed 8′
Lower: Melodia 8′
      Diapason 8′

Pedal: 16′, 8′
Vibrato: On Full

DRAWBAR ORGANS
Upper: 60-8856-364
Lower: (00) 6523-454 (0)

Pedal: 6 (4)
Vibrato: On Full

Johann Strauss

Moderate Waltz

Saint Anthony Chorale

ELECTRONIC ORGANS
Upper: Flutes 16', 8'
   String 8'
Lower: Diapason 8'

Pedal: 16'
Vibrato: Off

DRAWBAR ORGANS
Upper: 40-5545-336
Lower: (00) 5500-320 (0)

Pedal: 4 (3)
Vibrato: Off

Joseph Haydn

Comedians' Galop

ELECTRONIC ORGANS
Upper: Trumpet 8′ Pedal: 8′
Lower: Diapason 8′ Vibrato: On Full

DRAWBAR ORGANS
Upper: 00-7677-540 Pedal: 4 (3)
Lower: (00)-5431-210 (0) Vibrato: On Full

Very bright

Dmitri Kabalevsky

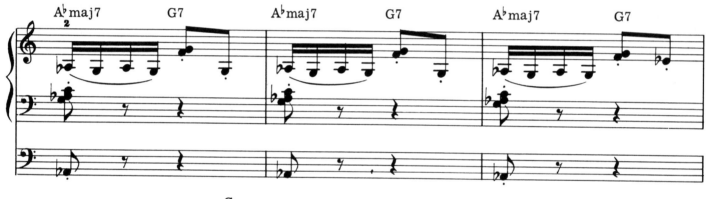

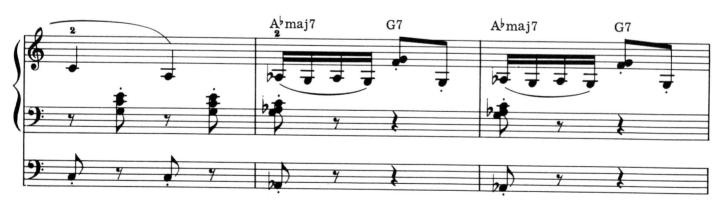

COMEDIANS GALOP - Kabalevsky

Notturno
Theme from String Quartet No. 2

ELECTRONIC ORGANS
Upper: Flute 8′   Pedal: 8′
Lower: Melodia 8′   Vibrato: On Full

DRAWBAR ORGANS
Upper: 008200-000   Pedal: 3 (2)
Lower: (00) 4302-000 (0)   Vibrato: On Full

Alexander Borodin

Mighty Lak' A Rose

ELECTRONIC ORGANS
Upper: Clarinet 8′   Pedal: 8′
Lower: Melodia 8′   Vibrato: On Full

DRAWBAR ORGANS
Upper: 00-8040-400   Pedal 3 (2)
Lower: (00) 43-03-000 (0)   Vibrato.. On Full

Ethelbert Nevin

Slowly and gently

Sweet-est lit-tle fel-ler, Ev-'ry bod-y knows; Dun-no what to call him, But he's might-y lak' a rose!

Look-in' at his Mam-my With eyes so shin-y blue, Make you think that heav-'n is com-in' close to you!

W'en he's there a sleep-in', In his li'l'___ place, Think I see the an-gels Look-in' thro' the lace;

We'n the dark is fall - in' W'en the shad-ows creep, Then they come on tip-toe To kiss 'im in his sleep.

Fine

rit.

D. C. al Fine

Kiss Me Again

ELECTRONIC ORGANS
Upper: Flutes 16′, 8′   Pedal: 16′
        String 8′   Vibrato: Off
Lower: Diapason 8′

DRAWBAR ORGANS
Upper: 40-5545-336   Pedal: 4 (3)
Lower: (00) 5500-320 (0)   Vibrato: Off

Slow waltz

Victor Herbert

Sweet sum - mer - breeze, whis - per - ing trees,

Stars shin - ing soft - ly a - bove; ___

Ros - es in bloom, waft - ed per - fume,

Sleep - y birds dream - ing of love. ___

Look Down That Lonesome Road

ELECTRONIC ORGANS
Upper: Flutes 16', 8'
String 8'
Lower: Diapason 8'

Pedal: 16'
Vibrato: Off

DRAWBAR ORGANS
Upper: 40-5545-336
Lower: (00) 5500-320 (0)

Pedal: 4 (3)
Vibrato: Off

Traditional

On The Banks Of The Wabash

ELECTRONIC ORGANS
Upper: Clarinet 8'   Pedal: 8'
Lower: Melodia 8'   Vibrato: On Full

DRAWBAR ORGANS
Upper: 00-8040-400   Pedal 3 (2)
Lower: (00) 43-03-000 (0)   Vibrato: On Full

Paul Dresser

Deep River

ELECTRONIC ORGANS
Upper: String 8′   Pedal: 8′
Lower: Melodia 8′   Vibrato: On Full

DRAWBAR ORGANS
Upper: 00 8222-232   Pedal: 3 (2)
Lower: (00) 4302-000 (0)   Vibrato: On Full

Slowly

Spiritual

Nobody Knows The Trouble I've Seen

ELECTRONIC ORGANS
Upper: Flutes 16′, 8′ 4′   Pedal: 16′, 8′
        Strings 8′   Vibrato: On Full
        Reed 8′
Lower: Melodia 8′
        Diapason 8′

DRAWBAR ORGANS
Upper: 60-8856-364   Pedal: 6 (4)
Lower: (00) 6523-454 (0)   Vibrato: On Full

Spiritual

Yankee Doodle Dandy

ELECTRONIC ORGANS
Upper: Flutes 16′, 8′ 4′
       Strings 8′
       Reed 8′
Lower: Melodia 8′
       Diapason 8′

Pedal: 16′, 8′
Vibrato: On Full

DRAWBAR ORGANS
Upper: 60-8856-364
Lower: (00) 6523-454 (0)

Pedal: 6 (4)
Vibrato: **On Full**

Lively

George M. Cohan

I'm a Yan - kee Doo - dle Dan - dy,
Yan - kee Doo - dle do or die;
Real live neph - ew of my Un - cle Sam's,
Born on the Fourth of Ju - ly.

In The Good Old Summertime

ELECTRONIC ORGANS
Upper: Flutes 16', 8' 4'   Pedal: 16', 8'
      Strings 8'   Vibrato: On Full
      Reed 8'
Lower: Melodia 8'
      Diapason 8'

DRAWBAR ORGANS
Upper: 60-8856-364   Pedal: 6 (4)
Lower: (00) 6523-454 (0)   Vibrato: On Full

Ren Shields

George Evans

Merry waltz tempo

In the good old sum - mer time,
In the good old sum - mer time,
Stroll - ing thro' the shad - y
lanes With your ba - by mine;

Vilia

from "The Merry Widow"

ELECTRONIC ORGANS
Upper: Clarinet 8'   Pedal: 8'
Lower: Melodia 8'   Vibrato: On Full

DRAWBAR ORGANS
Upper: 00-8040-400   Pedal 3 (2)
Lower: (00) 43-03-000 (0) Vibrato: On Full

Moderately

Franz Lehar

Vi - lia, my Vi - lia, I love on - ly thee,

And in thy eyes lies the whole world for me.

Life here be - low would be oh, so di - vine

If I could just make you mine.

Wait Till The Sun Shines Nellie

ELECTRONIC ORGANS
Upper: Flutes 16', 8' 4'   Pedal: 16', 8'
    Strings 8'   Vibrato: On Full
    Reed 8'
Lower: Melodia 8'
    Diapason 8'

DRAWBAR ORGANS
Upper: 60-8856-364   Pedal: 6 (4)
Lower: (00) 6523-454 (0)   Vibrato: On Full

Andrew B. Sterling

Harry Von Tilzer

Lively

Hello My Baby

ELECTRONIC ORGANS
Upper: Flutes 16′, 8′ 4′   Pedal: 16′, 8′
    Strings 8′   Vibrato: On Full
    Reed 8′
Lower: Melodia 8′
    Diapason 8′

DRAWBAR ORGANS
Upper: 60-8856-364   Pedal: 6 (4)
Lower: (00) 6523-454 (0)   Vibrato: On Full

Lively ragtime

Howard and Emerson

America, The Beautiful

ELECTRONIC ORGANS
Upper: Flutes 16′, 8′
String 8′
Lower: Diapason 8′
Pedal: 16′
Vibrato: Off

DRAWBAR ORGANS
Upper: 40-5545-336
Lower: (00) 5500-320 (0)
Pedal: 4 (3)
Vibrato: Off

Katherine L. Bates

Samuel A. Ward

Thanksgiving Hymn

ELECTRONIC ORGANS
Upper: Flutes 16', 8'
String 8'
Lower: Diapason 8'
Pedal: 16'
Vibrato: Off

DRAWBAR ORGANS
Upper: 40-5545-336
Lower: (00) 5500-320 (0)
Pedal: 4 (3)
Vibrato: Off

Moderately

Traditional Dutch Air

We gath-er to-geth-er to ask the Lord's bless-ing, He chast-ens and hast-ens His will to make known; The wick-ed op-press-ing now cease them from dis-tress-ing, Sing prais-es to His name,_____ He for-gets not His own.

O Come All Ye Faithful

(Adeste Fideles)

ELECTRONIC ORGANS
Upper: Flutes 16′, 8′   Pedal: 16′
      String 8′   Vibrato: Off
Lower: Diapason 8′

DRAWBAR ORGANS
Upper: 40-5545-336   Pedal: 4 (3)
Lower: (00) 5500-320 (0)   Vibrato: Off

Traditional

Auld Lang Syne

ELECTRONIC ORGANS
Upper: Flutes 16′, 8′ 4′   Pedal: 16′, 8′
       Strings 8′   Vibrato: On Full
       Reed 8′
Lower: Melodia 8′
       Diapason 8′

DRAWBAR ORGANS
Upper: 60-8856-364   Pedal: 6 (4)
Lower: (00) 6523-454 (0)   Vibrato: On Full

Scotch Air

6/95 (20402)